The **Graham Kendrick**
Psalm Collection

We hope you enjoy *The Graham Kendrick Psalm Collection*.
Further copies are available
from your local Kevin Mayhew stockist.

In case of difficulty, or to request a catalogue,
please contact the publisher direct by writing to:

The Sales Department
WORLD WIDE WORSHIP
Buxhall
Stowmarket
Suffolk IP14 3BW

Phone 01449 737978
Fax 01449 737834
E-mail info@kevinmayhewltd.com

This collection features songs taken from classic Kendrick albums including *Shine Jesus Shine*, *Is anyone Thirsty?* and *Crown Him, The Worship Musical.*

First published in Great Britain in 2002 by world wide worship.

© Copyright 2002 world wide worship.

ISBN 1 84003 863 2
ISMN M 57004 988 2
Catalogue No: 1400312

0 1 2 3 4 5 6 7 8 9

Cover design by Angela Selfe

Printed and bound in Great Britain

Important Copyright Information

The Publishers wish to express their gratitude to the copyright owners who have granted permission to include their copyright material in this book. Full details are indicated on the respective pages.

The **words** of most of the songs in this publication are covered by a **Church Copyright Licence** which is available from Christian Copyright Licensing International. This allows local church reproduction on overhead projector acetates, in service bulletins, songsheets, audio/visual recording and other formats.

The **music** in this book is covered by the additional **Music Reproduction Licence** which is issued by CCLI in the territories of Europe and Australasia. You may photocopy the music and words of the songs in the book provided:

> You hold a current Music Reproduction Licence from CCLI.

> The copyright owner of the song you intend to photocopy is included in the Authorised Catalogue List which comes with your Music Reproduction Licence.

The Music Reproduction Licence is **not** currently available in the USA or Canada.

Full details of CCLI can be obtained from their Web site (www.ccli.com) or you can contact them direct at the following offices:

Christian Copyright Licensing (Europe) Ltd
PO Box 1339, Eastbourne, East Sussex, BN21 1AD, UK
Tel: +44 (0)1323 417711; Fax: +44 (0)1323 417722; E-mail: info@ccli.co.uk

CCL Asia-Pacific Pty Ltd (Australia and New Zealand)
PO Box 6644, Baulkham Hills Business Centre, NSW 2153, Australia
Tel: +61 (02) 9894-5386; Toll Free Phone: 1-800-635-474
Fax: +61 (02) 9894-5701; Toll Free Fax: 1-800-244-477
E-mail executive@ccli.co.au

Christian Copyright Licensing Inc
17201 NE Sacramento Street, Portland, Oregon 97230, USA
Tel: +1 (503) 257 2230; Toll Free Phone: 1 (800) 234 2446;
Fax: +1 (503) 257 2244; E-mail executive@ccli.com

Please note, all texts and music in this book are protected by copyright and if you do <u>not</u> possess a licence from CCLI they may <u>not</u> be reproduced in any way for sale or private use without the consent of the copyright owner.

Foreword

The Psalms have been spiritual food and drink to millions for thousands of years. Though most familiar to us as text on the page, they were originally sung, and whilst there is no record of the original musical settings, over centuries different generations have given them their own soundtracks. This is a collection of some of the songs I have written over the years which have their origin and inspiration in the Psalms. In this selection the mood is joyful and uplifting, with an emphasis on proclaiming hope for the world, unity and transformation through the power of God's love.

GRAHAM KENDRICK

CONTENTS

1 Christ is King of all creation

Psalm 24, 93, 97 and 99

Words and Music: Graham Kendrick

1. Christ is King of all cre-a-tion, we pro-claim his king-dom here; call-ing you to come and serve him with rev-'rent fear.
2. We pro-claim that Christ is wor-thy to re-ceive the high-est throne, Let all pow'rs of earth and hea-ven serve him a-lone.

For the earth is

Leader: We are here to celebrate Jesus, the King of kings and Lord of lords. We invite you to join with believers all around the world, and with the whole company of heaven, to proclaim his kingdom of justice and joy, as we declare:

Leader: 1. Let the heavens rejoice!
2. Over governments, kings and rulers,

(2nd time) For he is exalted over all the nations.

(All) The Lord reigns!   The Lord reigns!

1. Let the earth be glad!
2. Over all powers, all authorities

F/G Let the nations tremble!

The Lord reigns!   The Lord reigns!

Let his people in every place proclaim:

The Lord reigns!   The Lord reigns!

(All: shouts and cheers)

2 Declare his glory

Psalm 96

Words and Music: Graham Kendrick

Declare his glo - ry, de-clare his glo - ry, de-clare his glo - ry a - mong the na - tions. na - tions.

Tell of his

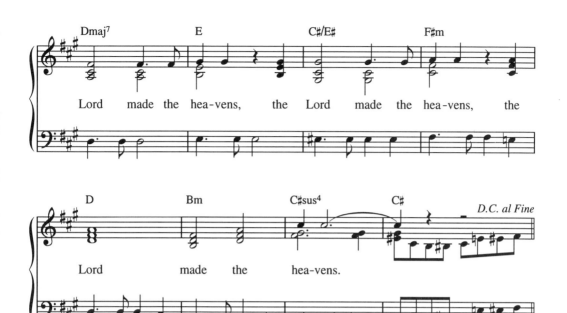

Lord made the hea-vens, the Lord made the hea-vens, the

Lord made the hea-vens.

D.C. al Fine

3 Far and near

Say it loud

Psalm 96 and 98

Words and Music: Graham Kendrick

world   what God has   done;   say   it

loud,   praise his   name,   let the earth re-joice–

for   the   Lord   reigns.

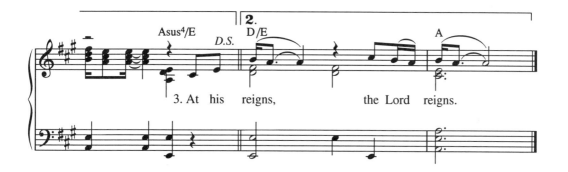

3. At   his   reigns,   the Lord   reigns.

3.   At his name, let praise begin;
oceans roar, nature sing,
for he comes to judge the earth
in righteousness and in his truth.

4 From where the sun rises

Psalm 134

Words and Music: Graham Kendrick

1. From where the sun ri - ses, e - ven to the

place it goes down — we're giv-ing you praise,

giv-ing you praise. From sun - kissed is-lands

and e-ven where the cold wind blows – we're giv-ing you

2. We're lifting our faces,
   looking at the One we all love –
   we're giving you praise,
   giving you praise.
   All colours and races
   joining with the angels above –
   we're giving you praise,
   giving you praise.

5 God, be gracious

Psalm 67

Words and Music: Graham Kendrick

God, be gra - cious and bless us and make your face shine on us: let your ways be known, your sal - va - tion shown all o - ver the earth; let your ways be known, your sal - va - tion shown all o - ver the earth.

Chorus

May the peo - ples praise you, O God, may all the peo -

6 God is great

Psalm 104

Words and Music: Graham Kendrick and Steve Thompson

ma-jes-ty bright, for he wraps him-self in a gar-ment of light. He

spreads out the hea-vens, his pa-lace of stars, and rides on the wings of the

wind. sings.

2. What marvellous wisdom the Maker displays,
the sea vast and spacious, the dolphins and whales.
The earth full of creatures, the great and the small,
he watches and cares for them all.

3. The rain forest canopies darken the skies,
cathedrals of mist that resound with the choirs
of creatures discordant, outrageous, ablaze
in colourful pageants of praise.

4. Above his creation the Father presides.
The pulse of the planets, the rhythm of tides.
The moon marks the seasons, the day follows night,
yet he knows ev'ry beat of my heart.

5. Let cannons of thunder salute their acclaim,
the sunsets fly glorious banners of flame,
the angels shout 'holy' again and again
as they soar in the arch of the heavens.

7 How good and how pleasant

Psalm 133

Words and Music: Graham Kendrick

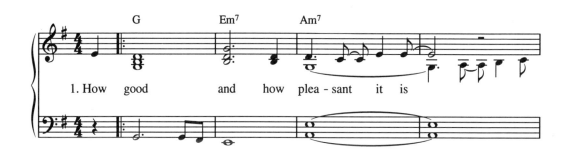

1. How good and how plea-sant it is

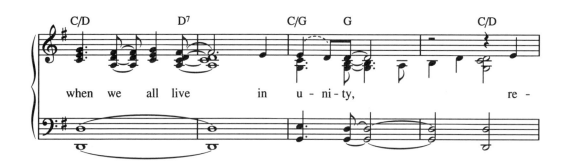

when we all live in u - ni - ty, re -

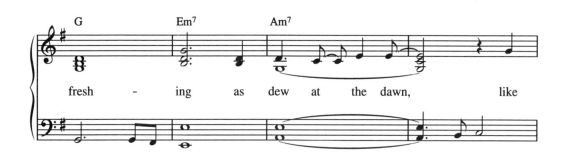

fresh - ing as dew at the dawn, like

rare a - noint - ing oil up - on the head.

2. How deep are the rivers that run
   when we are one in Jesus
   and share with the Father and Son
   the blessings of his everlasting life.

8 Lift up your heads

Psalm 24

O you gates

Words and Music: Graham Kendrick

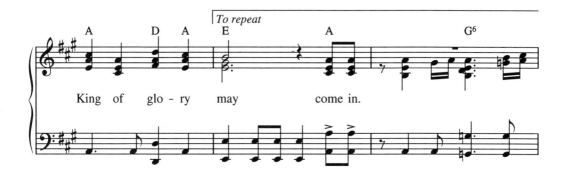

King of glo - ry may come in.

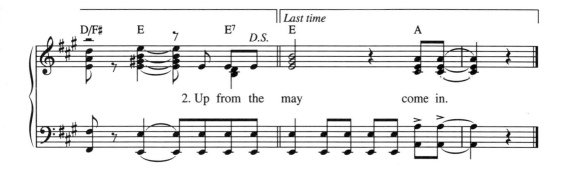

2. Up from the may come in.

2. Up from the dead he ascends,
   through ev'ry rank of heav'nly power.
   Let heaven prepare the highest place,
   throw wide the everlasting doors.

3. With trumpet blast and shouts of joy,
   all heaven greets the risen King.
   With angel choirs come line the way,
   throw wide the gates and welcome him.

9 Lord, we come in your name

Join our hearts

Psalm 133

Words and Music: Graham Kendrick

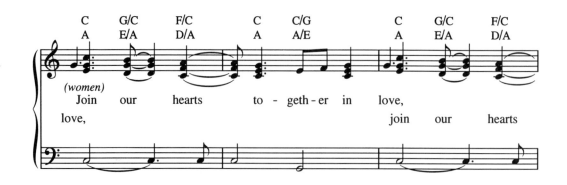

(women)
Join our hearts to-geth-er in love,

love, join our hearts

join our hearts

to-geth-er in love, (all) for there the

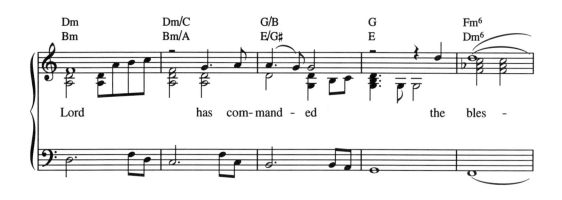

Lord has com-mand-ed the bles -

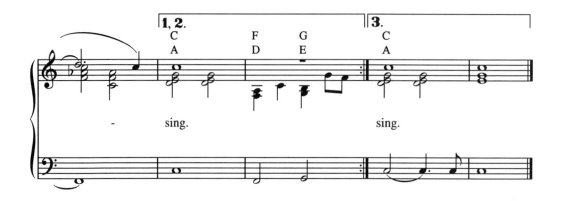

- sing. sing.

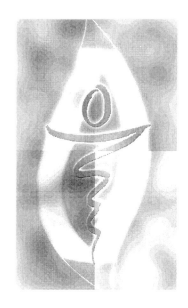

10 My heart is full

All the glory

Psalm 45

Words and Music: Graham Kendrick

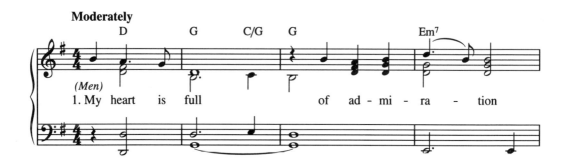

(Men)
1. My heart is full of ad - mi - ra - tion

for you, my Lord, my God and King.

(All)
Your ex - cel - lence, my in - spi - ra - tion,

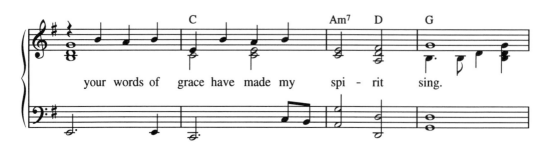

your words of grace have made my spi - rit sing.

2. *(Men)*   You love what's right and hate what's evil,
           therefore your God sets you on high,
(Women) and on your head pours oil of gladness,
           while fragrance fills your royal palaces.

3. *(All)*   Your throne, O God, will last for ever,
           justice will be your royal decree.
           In majesty, ride out victorious,
           for righteousness, truth and humility.

11 Open the gates

Psalm 24

Words and Music: Graham Kendrick

O - pen the gates for the King of kings. (O - pen the gates for the

King of kings!) *(All)* O - pen the gates for the King of kings.

(O - pen the gates for the) *(All)* King of kings.

Pre - pare the way of the

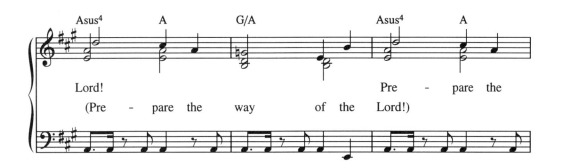

Lord!
(Pre - pare the way of the Lord!) Pre - pare the

way *(All)* of the Lord! Ho -

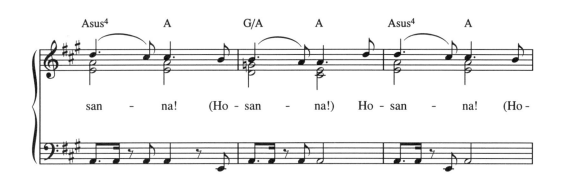

san - na! (Ho - san - na!) Ho - san - na! (Ho -

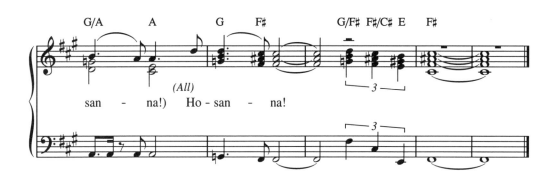

(All)
san - na!) Ho - san - na!

12 Sing a new song

Psalm 149

Words and Music: Graham Kendrick

Sing a new song, (sing a new song,) sing to the Lord a new song, (sing to the Lord a new song,) his praise in the as - sem - bly of the saints.

Sing a

1. Let Is - rael re - joice in their
2. The Lord takes de - light in his

13 To you, O Lord, I lift up my soul   *Psalm 25*

Words and Music: Graham Kendrick

1. To you, O Lord, I lift up my soul.
2. Show me your ways and teach me your paths.

In you I trust, O my God.
Guide me in truth, lead me on;

Do not let me be put to shame,
for you're my God, you are my Sa - viour.

nor let my e - ne - mies tri - umph o - ver me.
My hope is in you each mo - ment of the day.

Chorus
No one whose hope is in you

14 Welcome the King

Psalm 24

Words and Music: Graham Kendrick

1. Wel-come the King, wel-come the King, wel-come the King, wel-come the King,
2. Who is this King, who is this King, who is this King, who is this King,

wel-come the King who comes in the name of the Lord.
who is this King who comes in the name of the Lord?

Wel-come the King, wel-come the King, wel-come the King, wel-come the King,
Who is this King, who is this King, who is this King, who is this King,

wel-come the King who comes in the name of the Lord.
who is this King who comes in the name of the Lord?

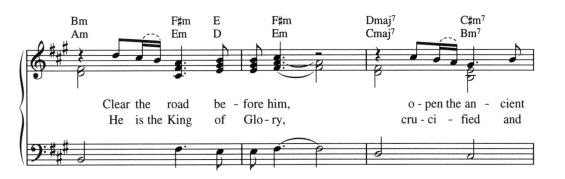

Clear the road be - fore him, o - pen the an - cient
He is the King of Glo - ry, cru - ci - fied and

doors, let ev-'ry heart re - ceive him:
ri - sen; he is the Lord Al - migh-ty:

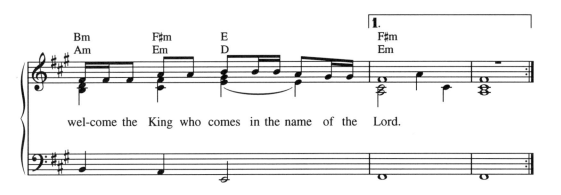

wel-come the King who comes in the name of the Lord.

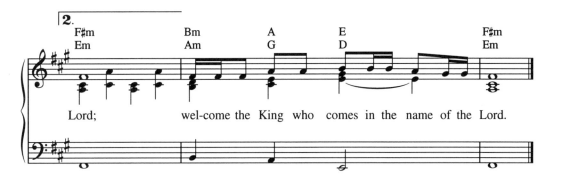

Lord; wel-come the King who comes in the name of the Lord.

15 When the Lord brought us back *Psalm 126*

Words and Music: Graham Kendrick

The **Graham Kendrick**
Prayer Song Collection
Book, CD & Cassette

Book: 1400313
ISMN M 57004 987 5

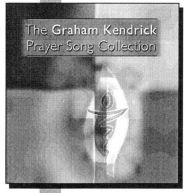

CD: 1490088
Cassette: 1480087

A dynamic collection of songs written to facilitate those times in worship when praise and adoration flow into intercession, when sung worship becomes sung prayer and particularly when there is a desire to pray for the neighbourhood and the nation.

A superb resource for praying churches as well as for personal devotions.

- *Come, let us worship Jesus (King of the nations)*
- *Hear, O Lord, our cry (Revive us again)*
- *Hear our cry*
- *If my people who bear my name*
- *Let it fill the room*
- *Lord, have mercy (Prayer song)*
- *Love of Christ, come now*
- *O Lord, the clouds are gathering*
- *Peace be to these streets*
- *Save the people*
- *Soften my heart, Lord*
- *Turn our hearts*
- *Turn to me and be saved*
- *Where two or three*
- *Who can sound the depths of sorrow*

Also available:

The **Graham Kendrick**
Psalm Collection
CD & Cassette

Featuring all of his worship songs from
this book:

CD: 1490089
Cassette: 1480088

- *Christ is King of all creation*
- *Declare his glory*
- *Far and near (Say it loud)*
- *From where the sun rises*
- *God, be gracious*
- *God is great*
- *How good and how pleasant*
- *Lift up your heads (O you gates)*
- *Lord, we come in your name (Join our hearts)*
- *My heart is full (All the glory)*
- *Open the gates*
- *Sing a new song (Psalm 149)*
- *To you, O Lord, I lift up my soul*
- *Welcome the King*
- *When the Lord brought us back (Psalm 126)*